아서 스타터 워크북 03

아서

집안일을 도와주다

글·그림 마크 브라운

롱테일북스

등장인물

D.W.

메리 무 카우를 좋아하는 아서의 여동생. 아서를 괴롭히는 게 취미이다.

엄마

아서의 엄마. 회계사로 언제나 바쁘게 일한다.

아빠

아서의 아빠. 다양한 요리로 늘 아서의 가족을 놀라게 한다.

메리 무 카우

D.W.가 가장 좋아하는 TV 프로그램의 주인공.

팔

아서 가족의 반려견. 사고뭉치이지만 아서를 잘 따른다.

Contents

ORANGE
JUICE
GRAPE
JELLY
crunch

토요일 아침, 아서는 놀고 싶었습니다.

"난 먼저 무엇을 해야 할까?" 그는 궁금해했습니다.

"내 친구들을 만날까? 나무 위의 집 안에 앉아 있을까?"

"엄마 아빠랑 얘기해 봐." D.W.가 말했습니다.

"오빠를 찾고 있어."

“너 거기 있었구나.” 아빠가 말했습니다.

“너는 오늘 집안일을 도와주어야겠구나.”

“하지만. . .” 아서가 말했습니다.

“네가 더 빨리 시작해야.” 엄마가 말했습니다. “더 빨리 마칠 수 있을 거야.”

"나는 내 방에서 뭐가 문제인지 모르겠는데." 아서는 혼잣말로 중얼거렸습니다.
"나는 모든 것이 어디에 있는지 알고 있어. 그게 중요한 것 아니야?"

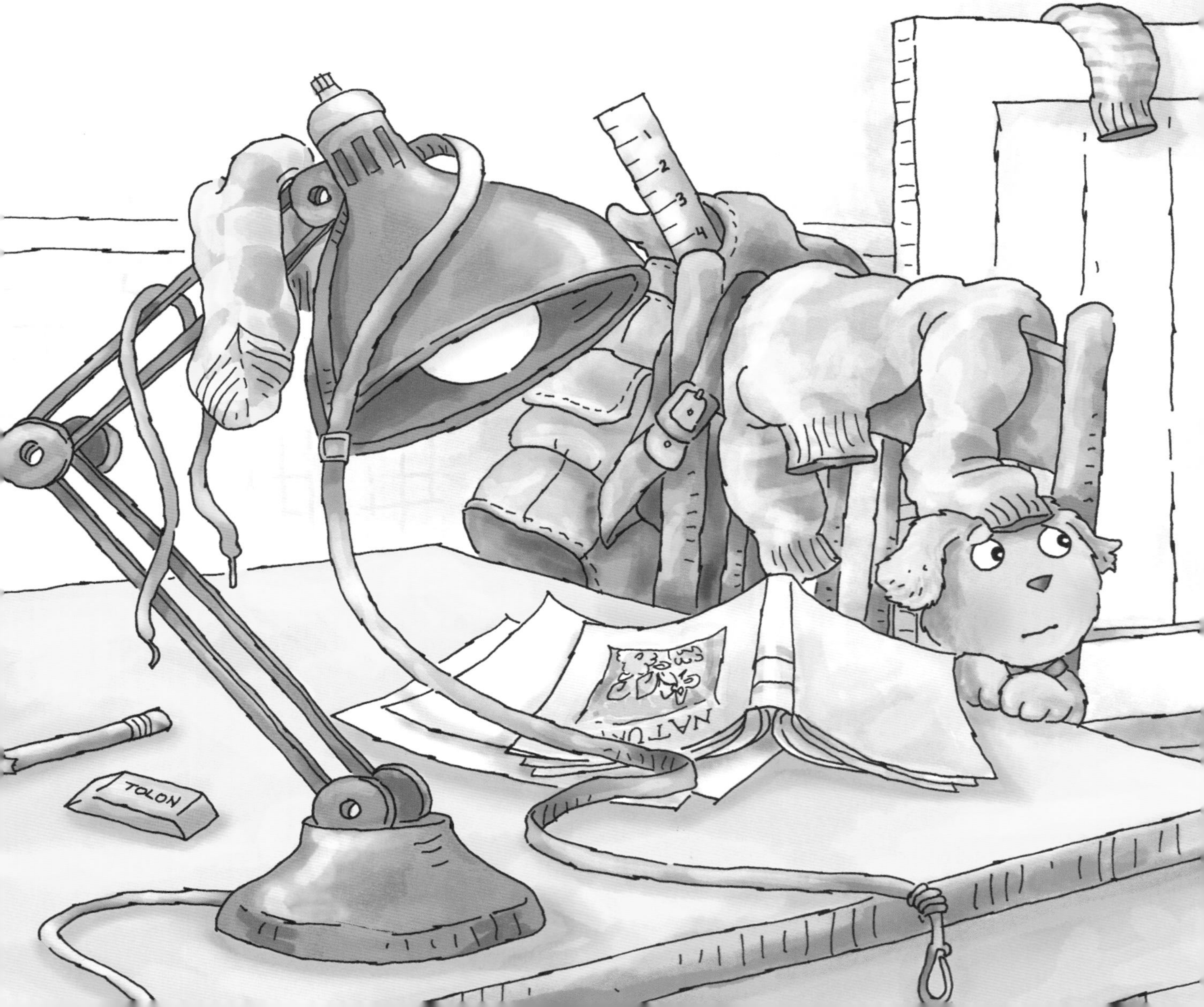

ROCKET KI

ELIZA

다음으로, 아서는 더러운 빨랫감을 모았습니다.

“내 것도 잊지 마.” D.W.가 말했습니다.

아서는 신음했습니다. “나는 네가 이렇게나 많고 다양한 옷을 입는다는 걸 믿을 수가 없어.”

아서는 쓰레기를 밖으로 가져가서 통 안에 쑤셔 넣었습니다.

“오-이런.” 그가 말했습니다. 그의 발이 붙어 버렸거든요.

그가 발을 떼는 것을 팔이 도와주었습니다.

chips

그다음에 아서는 팔을 목욕시켜야 했습니다.

“가만히 있어.” 팔이 버둥거리자 그가 말했습니다.

팔은 첨벙첨벙 물을 튀기고 또 튀겼고,

끝났을 때 누가 더 젖었는지 아서는 알 수 없었습니다.

식기세척기를 비울 때가 되자, D.W.가 돕고 싶어 했습니다.

아서가 혼자 한다면 더 빨리 할 수 있었지만, D.W.는 그를 내버려 두지 않았습니다.

"아무것도 떨어뜨리면 안 돼, 아서 오빠." 그녀가 말했습니다.

"접시랑 유리잔은 깨지기 쉬워."

Soap

그 이후에, 아서는 상자들을 다락방으로 옮겼습니다.

그는 이전처럼 빠르게 움직이고 있지 않았습니다.

“얼마나 많이 있는 거예요?” 그가 물었습니다.

“그냥 계속 옮기렴.” 엄마가 말했습니다. “일을 하다보면 나에게는 서류들이 많이 생긴단다.”

BOOKS

여전히 주워야 할 장난감들이 있었습니다.

“난 바이오닉 버니는 밖에 둘 거야.” 아서가 말했습니다. “그가 급하게 세상을 구해야 할 수도 있잖아.”

“그리고 메리 무 카우도 놔둬야지.” D.W.가 말했습니다. “그러면 그에게도 친구가 있을 거야.”

BOARDGAME

"아서 봤어요?" 아빠가 물었습니다.

"잠깐 못봤어요." 엄마가 말했습니다. "하지만 그 애는 매우 바빴어요."

“아서, 어디에 있니?” 아빠가 불렀습니다.

“숨을 필요 없단다.” 엄마가 말했습니다. “너는 오늘 큰 도움이 되었어. 그런데 우린 다 끝났어. 이제 네가 하고 싶은 대로 해도 된단다.”

하지만 이미 아서는 바로 그렇게 하고 있었습니다.

Activities

영어 원서를 총 세 개의 파트로 나누어,
각 파트별로 다양한 액티비티를 담았습니다.

각 파트의 영어 원서 페이지는 롱테일북스에서 출간된
'롱테일 에디션'을 기준으로 합니다!

Vocabulary Part 1

궁금해하다

wonder

말하다, 이야기하다

talk

찾다

look for

집

house

빨리, 곧

soon

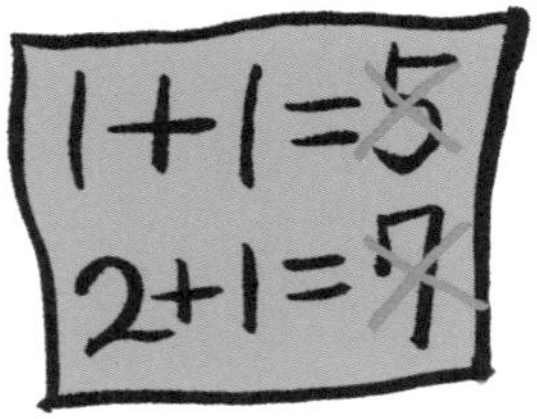

문제가 있는, 잘못된

wrong

방

room

중얼거리다

mutter

중요하다

matter

그다음으로; 그다음의

next

모으다

collect

더러운, 지저분한

dirty

빨랫감, 세탁물

laundry

잊다

forget

(끙 하는) 신음 소리를 내다

groan

입다

wear

많은

many

다른

different

Word Review Part 1

A 알파벳을 바르게 배열하여 그림에 맞게 단어를 완성해 보세요.

1

l a k t

2

r e a w

3

y t i d r

B 알파벳을 바르게 써넣어 그림에 알맞은 단어를 완성해 보세요.

1

co l le t

2

dif ren

3

f r et

C 그림을 보고 알맞은 단어를 퍼즐에서 찾은 뒤, 빈칸에 단어를 써 보세요.

v	a	w	r	o	n	g	f
k	l	o	y	m	b	d	y
z	i	n	j	o	c	r	t
g	x	d	w	q	u	h	z
r	m	e	c	r	a	o	n
o	w	r	s	l	y	u	k
a	y	m	x	t	i	s	i
n	e	x	t	j	u	e	r

1

groan

2

3

4
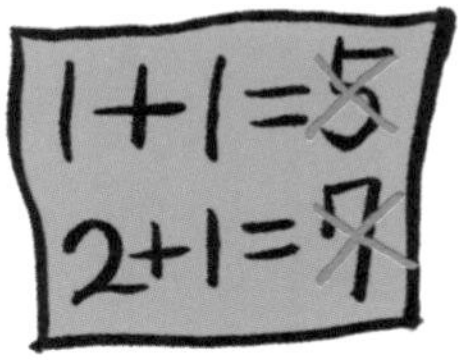

5

A 이야기의 순서에 맞게 번호를 적어 보세요.

Mom and Dad wanted Arthur to help out around the house.

1

On Saturday morning, Arthur wanted to play.

D.W. had lots of dirty laundry.

D.W. said that Mom and Dad were looking for Arthur.

B 각 단어에 알맞은 그림을 찾고, 이를 설명하는 문장을 찾아 바르게 이어 보세요.

wonder

Arthur collected D.W.'s dirty laundry with his.

room

Arthur wondered what he should do.

mutter

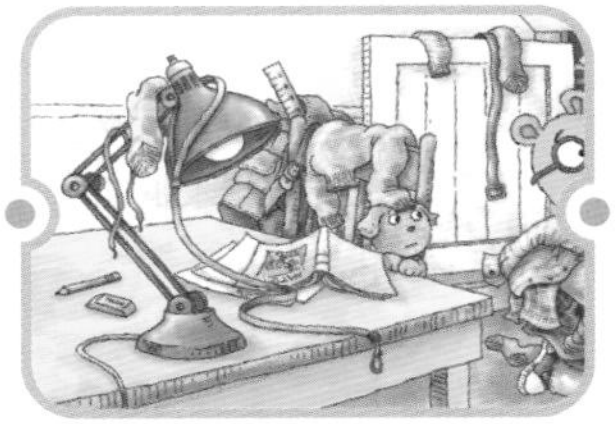

Arthur muttered to himself.

laundry

Arthur saw that everything was okay with his room.

C 다음 그림을 보고 아래의 단어를 알맞게 넣어 문장을 완성해 보세요.

groaned　　many　　forget

1 D.W. didn't want Arthur to ________ her laundry.

2 Arthur ________ as he collected D.W.'s laundry.

3 D.W. wore ________ different things.

D 책의 내용과 일치하면 TRUE에, 그렇지 않으면 FALSE에 동그라미를 그려 보세요.

1. It was Sunday morning. TRUE FALSE
2. Mom and Dad were looking for Arthur. TRUE FALSE
3. The sooner Arthur began to help out, the sooner he would be done. TRUE FALSE
4. Arthur didn't know where everything was in his room. TRUE FALSE

E 다음 질문에 대한 알맞은 답을 골라 보세요.

What did Arthur need to do?

a. See his friends

b. Sit in the tree house

c. Help out around the house

Let's Write! Part 1

A 우리말에 맞게 알맞은 짝을 찾아 바르게 연결하고 완성된 문장을 두 번씩 써 보세요.

1 You need to help out •	• where everything is.
2 The sooner you begin, •	• the sooner you'll be done.
3 I don't see •	• around the house.
4 I know •	• what's wrong with my room.

1 너는 집안일을 도와주어야겠구나.

You need to help out around the house.

2 네가 더 빨리 시작해야, 더 빨리 마칠 수 있을 거야.

3 나는 내 방에서 뭐가 문제인지 모르겠는데.

4 나는 모든 것이 어디에 있는지 알고 있어.

Vocabulary Part 2

가지고 가다 (과거형 took)

take

쓰레기

trash

쑤셔 넣다

stuff

(대형) 통

barrel

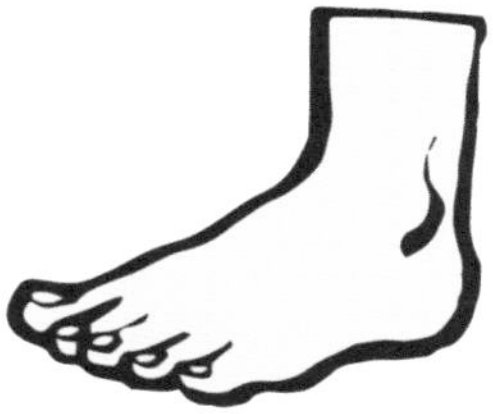

발

foot

움직일 수 없는, 꼼짝 못하는

stuck

자유로운

free

그대로 있다, 머무르다

stay

버둥대다, 꿈틀대다

squirm

첨벙거리다, 물을 튀기다

splash

젖은

wet

(짐을) 내리다, 빼내다

unload

식기세척기

dishwasher

혼자

alone

떨어뜨리다

drop

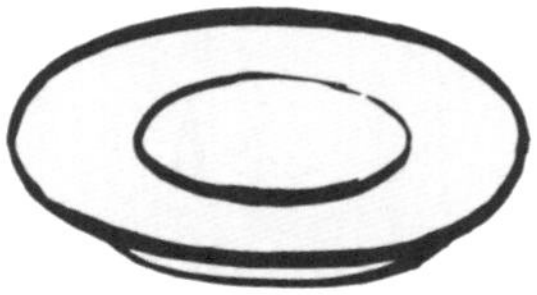

접시, 그릇

plate

유리잔, 유리

glass

깨어지다, 부서지다

break

Word Review Part 2

A 알파벳을 이어서 알맞은 그림과 연결하고, 빈칸에 완성된 단어를 써 보세요.

u

d e

t

t

s k

r c

a

p t

l o

w p

e

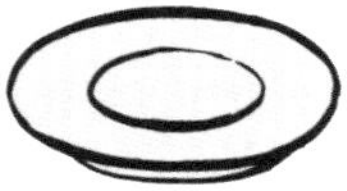

drop

B 그림을 보고 같은 색깔의 알파벳을 바르게 배열하여 빈칸에 써 보세요.

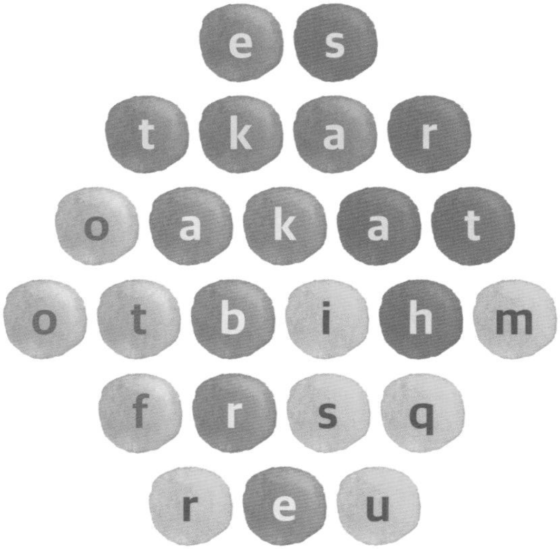

1

take

2

3

4

5

Wrap Up! Part 2

A 이야기의 순서에 맞게 번호를 적어 보세요.

Pal helped Arthur get free when his foot was stuck.

D.W. wanted to help Arthur unload the dishwasher.

Arthur took out the trash to put it in a barrel.

When Arthur gave Pal a bath, he splashed around.

B 두 개의 문장 중 오른쪽에 있는 그림을 바르게 설명하는 문장을 골라 보세요.

1

ⓐ Arthur's foot was stuck.

ⓑ Arthur's hand was stuck.

2

ⓐ Pal stayed still in the bathtub.

ⓑ Pal splashed in the bathtub.

3

ⓐ Arthur let D.W. help him.

ⓑ D.W. let Arthur work alone.

4

ⓐ D.W. warned Arthur not to drop the dishes.

ⓑ Arthur wanted to wash the dishes with D.W.

C 다음 그림을 보고 아래의 단어를 알맞게 넣어 문장을 완성해 보세요.

glasses unload alone

1. Arthur and D.W. are trying to ______ the dishwasher.

2. Arthur could have unloaded the dishes faster ______.

3. ______ break easily when they are dropped.

D 책의 내용과 일치하면 TRUE에, 그렇지 않으면 FALSE에 동그라미를 그려 보세요.

1. Pal's foot was stuck. TRUE FALSE
2. Arthur had to give Pal a bath. TRUE FALSE
3. Arthur was not sure who got wetter after Pal's bath. TRUE FALSE
4. D.W. didn't help Arthur unload the dishwasher. TRUE FALSE

E 다음 질문에 대한 알맞은 답을 골라 보세요.

What did Arthur say as Pal squirmed?

a "Uh-oh."

b "Stay still."

c "Bad dog!"

Let's Write! Part 2

A **오늘 공부한 문장을 따라 써 보세요.**

1 그의 발이 붙어 버렸거든요.

His foot was stuck.

2 그가 발을 떼는 것을 팔이 도와주었습니다.

Pal helped him get free.

3 아서는 팔을 목욕시켜야 했습니다.

Arthur had to give Pal a bath.

4 팔은 첨벙첨벙 물을 튀기고 또 튀겼습니다.

Pal splashed and splashed.

5 아무것도 떨어뜨리면 안 돼.

Don't drop anything.

6 접시랑 유리잔은 깨지기 쉬워.

Plates and glasses are easy to break.

Vocabulary Part 3

옮기다, 나르다 (과거형 carried)

carry

다락방

attic

이른, 일찍

early

묻다

ask

일

business

서류, 종이

paper

장난감

toy

줍다, 집어 들다

pick up

남기다, 떠나다

leave

구하다

save

급함, 서두름

hurry

친구, 손님

company

조금

a few

바쁜

busy

부르다, 외치다

call out

숨다

hide

큰

big

이미, 벌써

already

Word Review Part 3

A 그림을 보고 알파벳 속에서 맞는 단어를 찾아 빈칸에 써 보세요.

cakcarryeghbusinesshorhurrylshgitoylacompanykeiebigdl

1 

carry

2 

3 

4 

5 

6 

B 그림을 보고 알맞은 단어를 퍼즐에 완성한 뒤, 빈칸에 단어를 써 보세요.

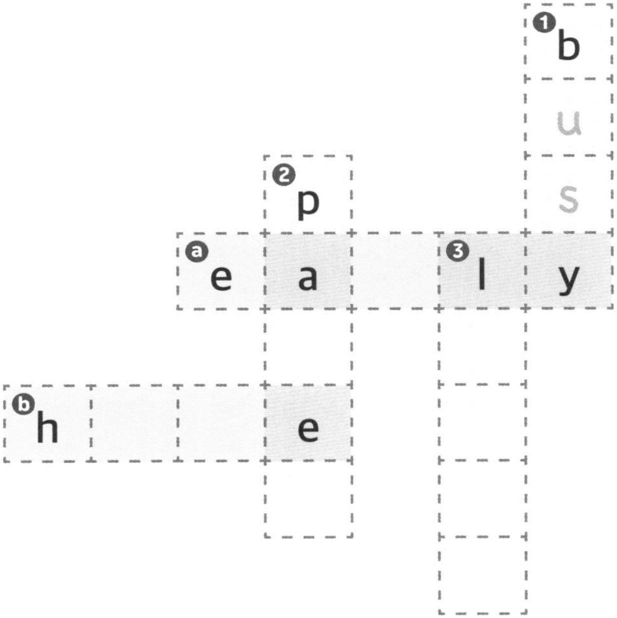

❶

busy

❷

ⓐ

ⓑ

❸

Wrap Up! Part 3

A 이야기의 순서에 맞게 번호를 적어 보세요.

Mom and Dad wanted to know where Arthur was.

Arthur was already doing what he wanted.

Arthur carried boxes of papers into the attic.

Dad was looking for Arthur.

B 그림의 각 부분을 올바르게 설명하는 문장을 찾아 빈칸에 맞는 기호를 넣어 보세요.

ⓐ Arthur had to pick up some toys.

ⓑ Bionic Bunny would have to save the world.

ⓒ D.W. wanted to leave Mary Moo Cow out, too.

ⓓ Mary Moo Cow would be company for Bionic Bunny.

C 다음 그림을 보고 아래의 단어를 알맞게 넣어 문장을 완성해 보세요.

business earlier asked

1. Arthur was moving faster ________ .

2. Arthur ________ how many boxes there were.

3. Mom collected a lot of papers in her ________ .

D 책의 내용과 일치하면 TRUE에, 그렇지 않으면 FALSE에 동그라미를 그려 보세요.

1. Arthur carried Mom's papers into the attic. TRUE FALSE
2. Arthur had to pick up toys. TRUE FALSE
3. Arthur had been busy all day. TRUE FALSE
4. Mom and Dad didn't think that Arthur was a big help. TRUE FALSE

E 다음 질문에 대한 알맞은 답을 골라 보세요.

Why did Arthur leave Bionic Bunny out?

a. Just in case Bionic Bunny had to hide
b. Just in case Bionic Bunny had to have company
c. Just in case Bionic Bunny had to save the world

Let's Write! Part 3

A 우리말에 맞게 네모 안에 있는 말을 바르게 배열해 보세요.

1 아서는 상자들을 다락으로 옮겼습니다.

boxes 상자들을	Arthur 아서는	carried 옮겼다	into the attic 다락으로

Arthur carried ______________________________ .

2 난 바이오닉 버니는 밖에 둘 거야.

leave 두다	I'll 나는 ~할 것이다	out 밖에	Bionic Bunny 바이오닉 버니를

______________________________ .

3 아서, 어디에 있니?

where 어디에	are 있니	Arthur, 아서	you 너는

______________________________ ?

4 숨을 필요 없단다.

hide 숨을	don't have to ~할 필요 없다	You 너는

.

5 너는 오늘 큰 도움이 되었어.

today 오늘	You 너는	a big help 큰 도움	were ~이 되었다

.

6 우린 다 끝났어.

all 다	done 끝난	We're 우리는 ~이다

.

Answers

Part 1

Word Review

A

1 

l a k t

talk

2 

r e a w

wear

3 

y t i d r

dirty

B

1 

collect

2 

different

3 

forget

C

v	a	w	r	o	n	g	f
k	l	o	y	m	b	d	y
z	i	n	j	o	c	r	t
g	x	d	w	q	u	h	z
r	m	e	c	r	a	o	n
o	w	r	s	l	y	u	k
a	y	m	x	t	i	s	i
n	e	x	t	j	u	e	r

1 

groan

2 

wonder

3 

next

4 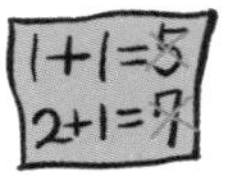

wrong

5 

house

Wrap Up!

A

3 

Mom and Dad wanted Arthur to help out around the house.

1 

On Saturday morning, Arthur wanted to play.

4 

D.W. had lots of dirty laundry.

2 

D.W. said that Mom and Dad were looking for Arthur.

B

wonder —  — Arthur wondered what he should do.

room — 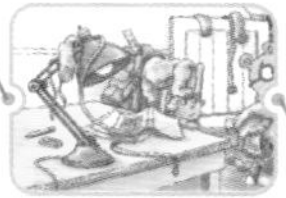 — Arthur saw that everything was okay with his room.

mutter —  — Arthur muttered to himself.

laundry —  — Arthur collected D.W.'s dirty laundry with his.

C

1 D.W. didn't want Arthur to forget her laundry.

2 Arthur groaned as he collected D.W.'s laundry.

3 D.W. wore many different things.

D 1 FALSE 2 TRUE 3 TRUE 4 FALSE

E c

Let's Write!

A

1	You need to help out	where everything is.
2	The sooner you begin,	the sooner you'll be done.
3	I don't see	around the house.
4	I know	what's wrong with my room.

Part 2

Word Review

A

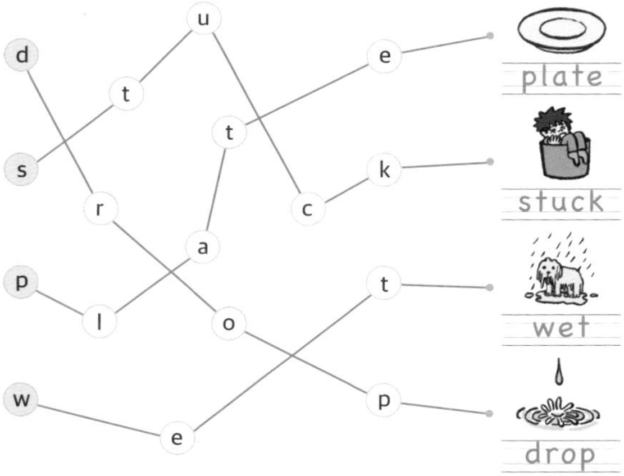

B

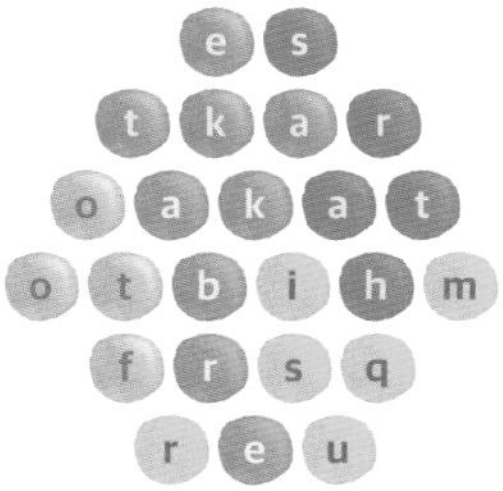

1

take

2

break

3

trash

4

foot

5

squirm

Wrap Up!

A

Pal helped Arthur get free when his foot was stuck.

D.W. wanted to help Arthur unload the dishwasher.

Arthur took out the trash to put it in a barrel.

When Arthur gave Pal a bath, he splashed around.

B 1 a 2 b 3 a 4 a

C

1 Arthur and D.W. are trying to unload the dishwasher.

2 Arthur could have unloaded the dishes faster alone.

3 Glasses break easily when they are dropped.

D 1 FALSE 2 TRUE 3 TRUE 4 FALSE

E b

Part 3
Word Review

A

cakcarryeghbusinesshorhurrylshgitoylacompanykeiebigdl

1 
carry

2 
business

3 
toy

4 
hurry

5 
company

6 
big

B

						❶ b
						u
			❷ p			s
		ⓐ e	a	r	❸ l	y
			p		e	
ⓑ h	i	d	e		a	
			r		v	
					e	

1 
busy

2 
paper

a 
early

b 
hide

3 
leave

Wrap Up!

A

3

Mom and Dad wanted to know where Arthur was.

4

Arthur was already doing what he wanted.

1

Arthur carried boxes of papers into the attic.

2

Dad was looking for Arthur.

B

C

1 Arthur was moving faster earlier .

2 Arthur asked how many boxes there were.

3 Mom collected a lot of papers in her business .

D 1 TRUE 2 TRUE 3 TRUE 4 FALSE

E c

Let's Write!

A

1 Arthur carried boxes into the attic.

2 I'll leave Bionic Bunny out.

3 Arthur, where are you?

4 You don't have to hide.

5 You were a big help today.

6 We're all done.

More Arthur Stories to Read!

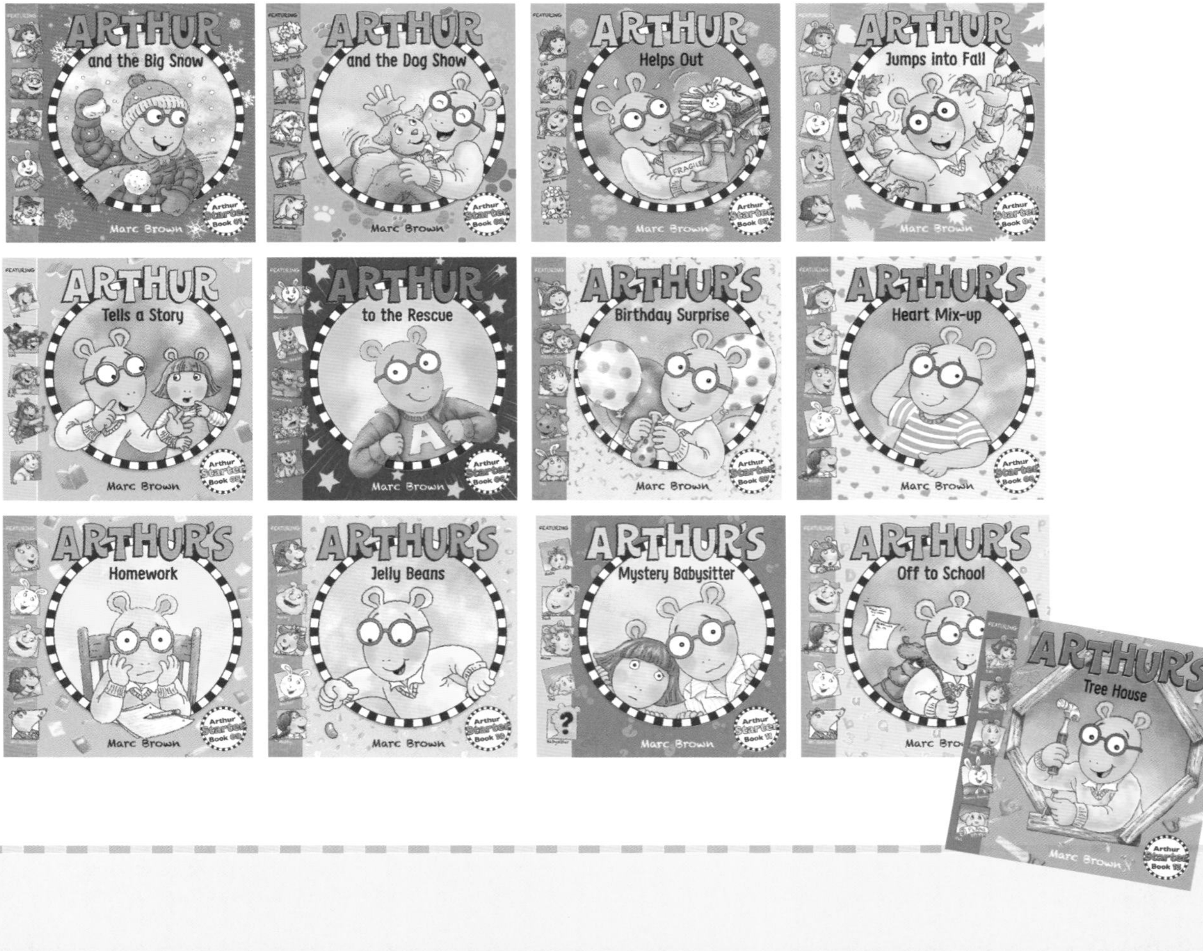

01 Arthur and the Big Snow
02 Arthur and the Dog Show
03 Arthur Helps Out
04 Arthur Jumps into Fall
05 Arthur Tells a Story
06 Arthur to the Rescue
07 Arthur's Birthday Surprise
08 Arthur's Heart Mix-Up
09 Arthur's Homework
10 Arthur's Jelly Beans
11 Arthur's Mystery Babysitter
12 Arthur's Off to School
13 Arthur's Tree House

재미있는 내용을 쉬운 문장과 간결한 표현으로 풀어 낸 기초 원서,
『아서 스타터(Arthur Starter)』 시리즈

아이들의 눈높이에 맞춘 유쾌한 이야기!
실생활에 바로 적용할 수 있는 영어 표현!

ARTHUR HELPS OUT

아서 집안일을 도와주다

초판 발행	2022년 1월 3일
글·그림	마크 브라운
번역및콘텐츠감수	유아름 정소이
콘텐츠제작참여	기나현 선생님(경기 고양 일산중) 김수정 선생님(경기 부천 계남초) 이재영 선생님(서울 영등포 영림초) 임소연 선생님(경기 동두천 생연초)
영문감수	Julie Tofflemire
책임편집	유아름 정소이 김보경
디자인	모희정 이강효
저작권	김보경
마케팅	김보미 정경훈
기획	김승규
펴낸이	이수영
펴낸곳	롱테일북스
출판등록	제2015-000191호
주소	04033 서울특별시 마포구 양화로 113(서교동) 3층
전자메일	helper@longtailbooks.co.kr
ISBN	979-11-91343-27-4 14740